PreScripts®

CURSIVE SENTENCES AND ART LESSONS

American History

PreScripts® Cursive Sentences and Art Lessons: American History

Illustrations by Kelly Digges

Published in the U.S.A. by Classical Conversations, Inc.
P.O. Box 909
West End, NC 27376

ISBN: 978-0-9884965-9-0

For ordering information, visit www.ClassicalConversationsBooks.com.
Printed in the United States of America

Table of Contents

A Note for Parents: Tools for the Journey

Introduction

The word "prescript" comes from the Latin words *prae* (meaning "before" or "in front of") plus *scribere* (meaning "to write"). The PreScripts® series from Classical Conversations MultiMedia is designed to precede—to come before—writing. Just as we learn to speak by mimicking our parents' words, we can learn to write well by copying the words that others have written. Even though coloring, drawing, tracing, and copying are simple tasks from an adult perspective, imitation is at the heart of a classical education. In order to learn how to write, children must first acquire fine motor skills and learn to sit still and follow instructions. They do so with the help of simple tasks like these. Rather than resorting to mindless busywork that isolates young children from their family's education, the PreScripts series is designed to initiate young learners into the world of knowledge they will inhabit as they mature.

Each book in the PreScripts series combines a functional design with excellent content. The goal of *PreScripts® Cursive Sentences and Art Lessons* is to take the building blocks of cursive writing (letters, words, and simple sentences) and funnel them into longer sentences and more writing practice. As they gain confidence and skill, your students will first trace each sentence and then write it, keeping the model nearby.

Our job as classical educators is to teach students to make the effort to be neat but preferably to aim higher by teaching them to write beautifully. Many schools no longer teach cursive writing, claiming that it is too difficult for young children to master. Teaching a child to write in cursive does require diligence and patience, but it has a number of compelling benefits. Research suggests that cursive writing more effectively develops manual skill and dexterity. Cursive may also aid students struggling with dyslexia or dysgraphia because 1) capital and lowercase letters are distinct; 2) each word is one fluid movement, so the child's rhythm is not disrupted by frequent pauses; and 3) letters like "b" and "d" are more difficult to reverse.

While they master the manual skill of writing, students will also reinforce writing and reading rules. They will begin to notice unusual punctuation—for example, hyphenated words at the end of a line or an ellipsis[...] to show that part of a quote has been eliminated—and will be less likely to stumble when they encounter these practices in other books. When your child becomes curious, take a moment to explain these rules. As a result, writing correctly will come more naturally to them when they compose their own sentences.

How to Use This Book

When children are learning to read and write, the 'what' matters as much as the 'how.' Parents are more likely to give up on cursive when the content seems frivolous, so Classical Conversations is pleased to offer cursive writing books that give the student plenty of practice using rich, meaningful content. With PreScripts cursive writing books, your student can become a confident writer while learning or reviewing important subject matter such as history sentences, passages of literature, and proverbs.

In this book, we focus on sentences about American history. By the time the book is completed, your child will have had the opportunity to master twenty-four history sentences about Christopher Columbus, the Missouri Compromise, and the Great Depression, among other topics. Pair this book with a unit study of American history or use it as a stand-alone resource.

To provide some variety for your child, art lessons are sprinkled throughout the book. Drawing will also help to develop the fine motor skills necessary for writing and provide practice in working independently. Your child will enjoy learning about elements of design and composition such as positioning, texture, point of view, and perspective, using images related to the sentences he is writing in cursive.

A basic pencil and eraser will be sufficient to complete these drawing lessons, but you may find it helpful to have a soft pencil (HB or 2B) and a hard pencil (2H) as well as a blending stump and a soft gum eraser. The exercises are simple enough for your child to do independently and will appeal to different senses and learning styles while continuing to reinforce the content of the history sentences.

Although variety is important, the key to mastering cursive is to practice every day. For best results, set aside a specific time each day for cursive practice. You choose the pace appropriate for your child. You can assign one page a day to a beginning student or assign two to four pages a day to an older or more experienced student. A very young student, or one who struggles with writing, might even do half a page a day until his or her fine motor skills become stronger, working up to a page or two a day. The pace is completely up to the parent.

If you choose to do one page a day, you should have enough pages for a complete school year, completing approximately four or five pages a week. If you participate in a Classical Conversations community, you can do four pages a week while your community meets and five pages a week the rest of the school year. Older children might do two pages a day and complete two books a year. If you would like your child to memorize the history sentences in this book, you can read through the sentences weekly to review or have your student do the same book twice.

The Journey in Perspective

The key to good writing is daily practice. The key to a heart that seeks truth, beauty, and goodness is providing quality content to copy. We hope you will find both in *PreScripts® Cursive Sentences and Art Lessons: American History*.

The goal of the PreScripts series is for your children to master the skills of copying and writing in the context of a biblical worldview, building on a second meaning of the word "prescript." A prescript can also mean a command, rule, or moral guideline. The Bible instructs parents to remember the commandments of God and teach them to their children.

Deuteronomy 6:6–9 (NIV) reads, "And these words which I command you today are to be in your heart. You shall teach them diligently to your children, and shall talk of them when you sit in your house, when you walk by the way, when you lie down, and when you rise up. You shall bind them as a sign on your hand, and they shall be as frontlets between your eyes. You shall write them on the doorposts of your house and on your gates." As this Scripture reminds us, writing, memorizing, and reciting are all forms of worship that we model for our children.

Let's get started!

Forming the Cursive Letters

Trace, then write each letter.

A a   *B b*   *C c*

D d   *E e*   *F f*

G g   *H h*   *I i*

J j   *K k*   *L l*

Using a Grid to Draw

One way that artists draw from a picture is to use a **grid**.

On your drawing paper, draw four* lines across and four lines down to form a blank grid. Use a hard pencil, which will make a light line.

To draw, just look at one square at a time and draw exactly what you see in that square. Fill in all your squares to match the squares of the original. Draw lightly at first so you can easily redraw a line with a darker pencil.

This method will help you get the basic lines in the right place for your drawing. Use a softer pencil to add the details to your drawing. Erase the grid lines to complete your drawing.

** If the drawing is very detailed, you can draw more lines across and down.

English ship in a gale

Using Mapping to Draw

Another way to start a sketch is to **map** what you will be drawing. This means to lightly draw "blobs" of similar shape and size compared to the main shapes in a drawing and then to draw in a more detailed shape.

The blobs are a guide to help you keep all the elements of your drawing the right size and in the right place. It works just like a map, highlighting the general shapes you will use.

Be sure to draw lightly (with a hard pencil if you have one) so that you can erase the guidelines later. Use a softer pencil to draw in the contour lines (the actual outlines or edges of the elements of the drawing).

In the art lessons that follow, you will be asked to draw some illustrations. You can choose either a grid or mapping to start drawing your illustration.

Each illustration relates to a card from the *Classical Acts & Facts History Cards* Timeline. If you have these cards, you might want to look at them while you draw. It may give you more details or ideas for coloring the finished drawing with colored pencils.

English ship in a gale

History Note 1(a) Trace, then write the sentence.

In 1492, Columbus made the first of four

trips to the Caribbean on three Spanish

ships manned the Niña, the Pinta, and the

Santa María.

History Note 1(b) Trace, then write the sentence.

In 1492, Columbus made the first of four

trips to the Caribbean on three Spanish

ships named the Niña, the Pinta, and the

Santa María.

Motion

English ship in a gale

In this composition, the artist has added a feeling of **motion** by placing the large boat in the center of the picture at an angle. See how it is leaning sideways? Notice that the boat is riding up a wave and is tilting to the left.

You can also tell that the water is moving. It looks as though it is churning up and down because the artist drew waves in the foreground, the area on the lower area of the picture close to you as you view the picture. Can you see how the horizon line, where the sky meets the sea, is not a straight line in this composition? It is made up of curves, which also helps create the sense that the waves are in motion.

How does this picture make you feel? Does it seem frightening? You can tell just by looking at this picture that this is not a safe boat ride. It is dangerous!

Try drawing this piece yourself. Be sure to shade the foreground darker than the background because this, along with the churning, tossing waves, helps create a threatening feeling in the composition.

Your drawing:

History Note 2(a) Trace, then write the sentence.

In 1620, the Pilgrims from Plymouth,

England signed the Mayflower Compact

before landing in Plymouth, Massachusetts.

History Note 2(b) Trace, then write the sentence.

In 1620, the Pilgrims from Plymouth,

England signed the Mayflower Compact

before landing in Plymouth, Massachusetts.

Proportion

Columbus sets sail for the Caribbean

This is an ocean scene with ships, but it is very different from the one we just looked at. The mood of this picture is much more relaxed. The water is calm. There is some movement in the water, but here it is rippling gently; there are no churning waves. The boats are sitting up straight, not tilted at an angle. Notice that there is only a slight movement on the large boat, where Columbus is about to kiss the hand of Queen Isabella of Spain.

The boats in the background are also sitting still, floating on a peaceful sea. Have you noticed how these smaller boats in the background seem farther away than the larger boats? Of course, this is not true, because all the boats are the same distance away from the viewer. This illusion was made by drawing the boats smaller and placing them behind the oars of the large ship in the foreground.

Proportion is a term describing the size of some parts of a drawing compared to other parts. These parts that make up a drawing are called elements. If you draw a small element next to one that is large, you are using proportion to create an illusion of distance in the picture. The larger element will look as if it is closer to you, and the smaller element will look as if it is farther away from you. Proportion makes a composition more interesting, adding a sense of depth to works of art.

Draw a scene with a large boat and a small boat. Does the larger one look closer to you than the smaller one?

Your drawing:

History Note 3(a) Trace, then write the sentence.

In 1773, colonists dressed as Mohawks

dumped tea from the British East India

Company into Boston Harbor.

History Note 3(b) Trace, then write the sentence.

In 1773, colonists dressed as Mohawks

dumped tea from the British East India

Company into Boston Harbor.

Point of View

Native Americans watching the colonists construct Fort James

See the Indians peeking out from the trees, watching the colonists build their fort? This makes the composition interesting. The artist used **point of view** in this illustration to make us feel as though we are right alongside those Indians!

Point of view refers to the perspective from which we see a scene. If an artist chooses to draw a picture from an unusual point of view, the scene becomes more intriguing.

The artist created this point of view by placing some trees in the foreground and some Indians almost beside us, the viewers. Don't you feel as though you are hiding behind the trees with the Indians? Since the trees are beside and above us, we feel as though we are peeking out but are still hidden from the view of the colonists in the picture. Isn't it fun to feel as though you are part of the action of the picture?

Pretend you are an Indian while you draw this scene.

Your drawing:

History Note 4(a) Trace, then write the sentence.

In 1776, the Continental Congress published

the Declaration of Independence in

Philadelphia, announcing the colonists'

intent to form a new nation.

History Note 4(b) Trace, then write the sentence.

In 1776, the Continental Congress published

the Declaration of Independence in

Philadelphia, announcing the colonists'

intent to form a new nation.

Diminishing Point

The sense of depth in this composition is created by the line of soldiers standing at attention. The line seems to stretch far away into the background, doesn't it?

Do you see the soldier in the lower right hand corner? He is the largest man in the scene. Each soldier in the line after him is slightly smaller than he is, right? You could draw a straight line at the feet of the line of soldiers, and a straight line at their heads, and these two lines would eventually meet at the **diminishing point** toward the back of the picture, on the horizon line. Artists keep the proportions in their compositions accurate by drawing lines like these.

When you draw this composition, begin by drawing such lines. First, draw a horizon line—a straight, horizontal line all the way across your paper and about two-thirds of the way up the page. Next, draw two lines where the feet and the heads of the soldiers are going to be. These two lines should meet at the horizon line. Now draw in the soldiers, fitting them in between the two lines. The soldiers should stand straight up, in line with the vertical edge of your paper.

General George Washington takes command of the American Army

Your drawing:

History Note 5(a) Trace, then write the sentence.

In 1789, in New York, George Washington was

granted the full powers and responsibilities of

the presidency by the U.S. Constitution.

History Note 5(b) Trace, then write the sentence.

In 1789, in New York, George Washington was

granted the full powers and responsibilities of

the presidency by the U.S. Constitution.

Projection Maps

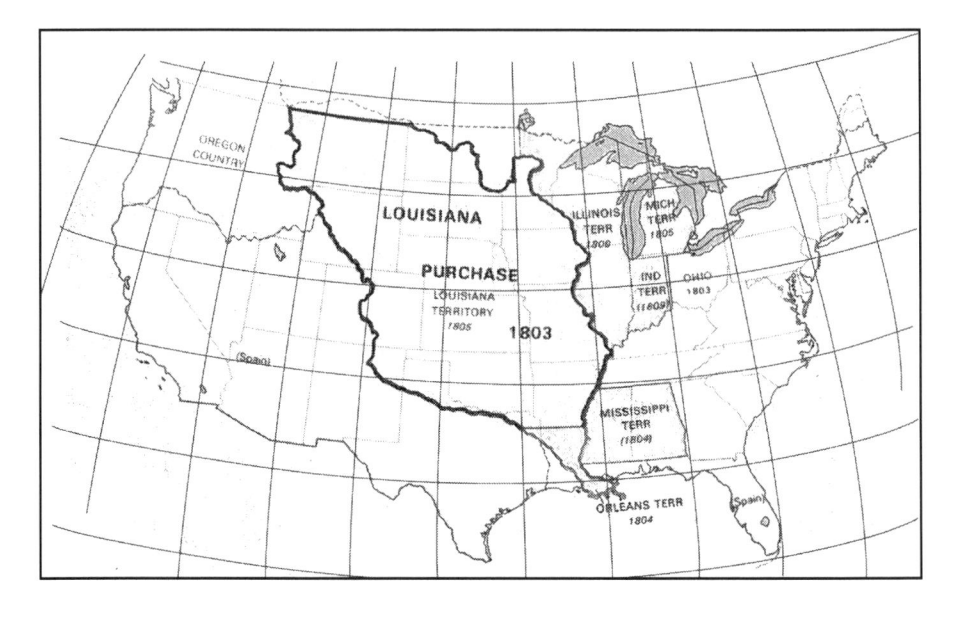

Projection map showing the Louisiana Purchase

Look at this map. Can you see that there are lines running up and down the page? Do they look straight? No, they don't. In fact, they look as though they would intersect if they continued upward, don't they?

The reason these vertical lines look as though they will meet is because the lines running across the map horizontally are curved. Can you see how they form the shape of a smile? Why are these horizontal lines curved? To show that we are looking at the surface of the world, which is a sphere.

The illustrator of this picture imagined how the land would fit onto the globe, and tried to draw it shaped by the sphere. This is called an equal-area **projection map**. Some maps are drawn with the lines straightened out, which makes the land at the top appear larger than it actually is. These are called Mercator projection maps.

Either way of drawing a map works well. When you look at a map, however, it is good to recognize which technique the cartographer (another word for 'map maker') used. This will help you know if the land appears bigger than it actually is. Whenever you look at a map from now on, try to tell which method the cartographer used.

Try drawing this map with the angled and curved lines of an equal-area projection map.

Your drawing:

History Note 6(a) Trace, then write the sentence.

In 1803, the purchase of Louisiana from

France prompted westward exploration by

pioneers, such as Lewis and Clark and

Congressman Davy Crockett.

History Note 6(b) Trace, then write the sentence.

In 1803, the purchase of Louisiana from

France prompted westward exploration by

pioneers, such as Lewis and Clark and

Congressman Davy Crockett.

Focal Point

Francis Scott Key sees the U.S. flag, the "Star-Spangled Banner"

This composition captures the moment when Francis Scott Key composed a poem that was later given the title "The Star-Spangled Banner." You may recognize the title because it is famous. It became the national anthem of the United States of America! Do you know the words to the song? It begins like this:

> Oh, say, can you see, by the dawn's early light,
> What so proudly we hail'd at the twilight's last gleaming?

What do you think they were hailing? The American flag, also known as the Star-Spangled Banner. Can you see it in this drawing? It is small, in the distance, and in the background.

In the original painting, you can see the sky's morning light, filled with colors of pink and gray. The artist placed the flag in the distance and made its edges blurry so that it is a bit hard to see. Notice, however, that lots of lines in the composition point right to that flag! For starters, Francis Scott Key's outstretched arm points directly at it. The horizon line also leads the viewer's eye to it. And can you see all that open space around the flag? All these factors make the flag the **focal point** of this composition. That means it is the point where your eye is directed to go and where your gaze wants to linger.

Try drawing this composition. Make the people and the ship in the foreground dark, but make the flag and the island in the background much lighter. This will help give your composition depth and direct the observer's eye to the focal point: the flag.

Your drawing:

History Note 1(c) Review. Trace, then write the sentence.

In 1492, Columbus made the first of four

trips to the Caribbean on three Spanish

ships named the Niña, the Pinta, and the

Santa María.

History Note 2(c) Review. Trace, then write the sentence.

In 1620, the Pilgrims from Plymouth,

England signed the Mayflower Compact

before landing in Plymouth, Massachusetts.

History Note 3(c) Review. Trace, then write the sentence.

In 1773, colonists dressed as Mohawks

dumped tea from the British East India

Company into Boston Harbor.

For practice, draw one of the art lessons again in this space.

History Note 4(c) Review. Trace, then write the sentence.

In 1776, the Continental Congress published

the Declaration of Independence in

Philadelphia, announcing the colonists'

intent to form a new nation.

History Note 5(c) Review. Trace, then write the sentence.

In 1789, in New York, George Washington was

granted the full powers and responsibilities of

the presidency by the U.S. Constitution.

History Note 6(c) Review. Trace, then write the sentence.

In 1803, the purchase of Louisiana from

France prompted westward exploration by

pioneers, such as Lewis and Clark and

Congressman Davy Crockett.

For practice, draw one of the art lessons again in this space.

History Note 7(a) Trace, then write the sentence.

The War of 1812 gave confidence to the U.S. to

write the Monroe Doctrine, warning Europeans

not to attempt to colonize the Americas.

History Note 7(b) Trace, then write the sentence.

The War of 1812 gave confidence to the U.S. to write the Monroe Doctrine, warning Europeans not to attempt to colonize the Americas.

Natural Body Positions

Discussing the Monroe Doctrine

Doesn't this composition remind you of a photograph? It is as though the artist captured a moment in time, taking a snapshot when no one was looking.

Look at the men in the picture. They are not lined up, facing the artist and standing still as they would be in a posed portrait. They are sitting or standing in relaxed, **natural body positions**. This creates the feeling that we are watching history take place, just exactly at the moment it is happening!

This picture shows these men gathered around a globe placed on a table. They are, in fact, in the middle of a conversation about the Monroe Doctrine. This is an important moment in United States history—much more exciting than the moment right after the conversation ended and the action was over. That is probably why the artist chose to capture it, don't you think?

Look at the expressions on the men's faces. Can you tell that they are making a difficult decision? Their faces are serious, aren't they? They are also focused on the globe and seem to be working hard on solving some problem.

Whenever you draw a scene, think about how you might capture an important moment in action. In fact, try to draw this scene or another moment in history. You might even draw a moment when your family had a serious discussion about an important decision.

Your drawing:

History Note 8(a) Trace, then write the sentence.

In 1820, Henry Clay worked out the Missouri

Compromise, allowing Missouri to enter the

Union as a slave state and Maine as a free

state.

History Note 8(b) Trace, then write the sentence.

In 1820, Henry Clay worked out the Missouri

Compromise, allowing Missouri to enter the

Union as a slave state and Maine as a free

state.

Drawing Maps

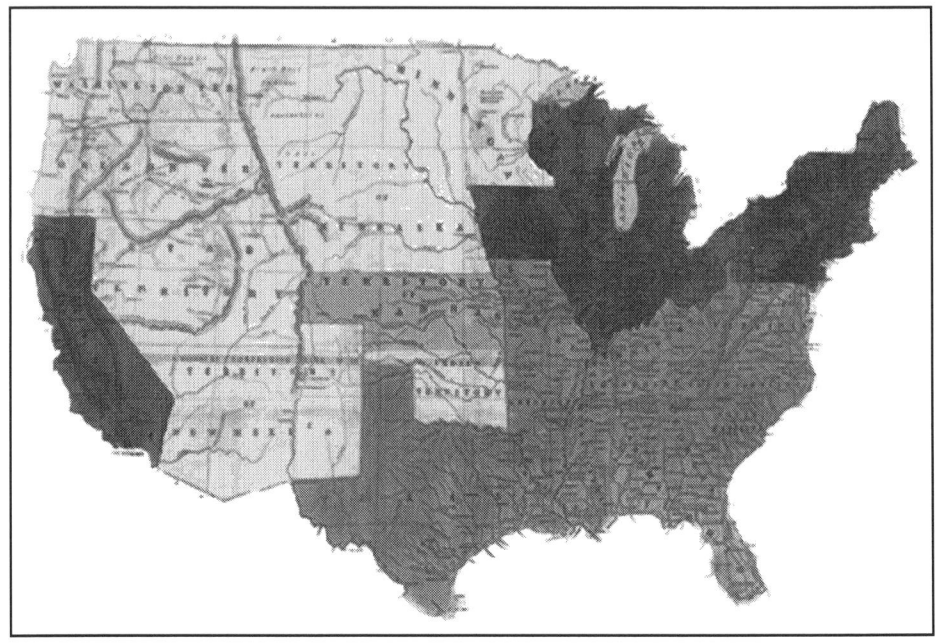

Map Key:

Free States

Slave States

Free Territories

Did you know there are ways to learn how to draw maps? For example, a good way to begin drawing the map of the United States pictured here would be to make the outline of the entire shape of the United States and then fill in the inside details.

Take a good look at this map. Name the types of lines you see. Do you see a straight line? A curved line? Some angled lines? Now, try finding some lines that run up and down through the map. Do you see that there is one that runs along California, one that runs from Montana to New Mexico, and one that runs from Minnesota down to Texas? If you draw these vertical lines within your outline of the whole shape first, then you can outline the remaining states!

The map on this card is from the mid-1800s, so it is a little different from the map of the United States today. Can you spot the differences?

You can begin to learn **drawing maps** from memory by practicing with the map of the United States. In the space below, draw this historical map or the current map of the United States.

Map of the United States showing free and slave states

Your drawing:

History Note 9(a) Trace, then write the sentence.

The Compromise of 1850, the Fugitive Slave Act, and the Dred Scott decision preceded the secession of the Southern states.

History Note 9(b) Trace, then write the sentence.

The Compromise of 1850, the Fugitive Slave

Act, and the Dred Scott decision preceded the

secession of the Southern states.

Form Showing Emotion

"End of the Trail" bronze statue by James Earle Fraser

Do you feel sad when you look at the drawing of this bronze sculpture? The artist has stirred that feeling in you. Can you see how? It is because of the postures of the man and the horse. They both slump forward, their heads hanging far lower than usual. Notice that the horse's feet are very close together. This helps us understand that the horse pictured here is taking small, difficult steps. This sculpture is an excellent example of **form showing emotion**.

During the 1838–1839 relocation of five of the Indian nations to the reservation in Oklahoma, the Native Americans and their horses were marched for 800 tortuous miles. They suffered extreme fatigue and starvation. Many died along the trip, appropriately named the Trail of Tears.

Through the positioning of the bodies of the Indian and his horse, the sculptor masterfully captures the feeling of despair and exhaustion the Indians experienced on the trail.

Draw this composition below. Begin by sketching the bowed line of the man's body and the curved lean of the horse's body.

Your drawing:

History Note 10(a) Trace, then write the sentence.

In 1853, after the Mexican War and the

Gadsden Purchase, President Polk's belief in

the doctrine of Manifest Destiny was realized.

History Note 10(b) Trace, then write the sentence.

In 1853, after the Mexican War and the

Gadsden Purchase, President Polk's belief in

the doctrine of Manifest Destiny was realized.

Centrally Positioned Figure

The United States Senate in 1850

In this composition, the artist captures an extremely important moment of debate in the United States government.

See how the artist placed the focal point of the composition—the man drawn the largest in the foreground—right in its center?

Look at the faces of all the men surrounding this central figure. See how their faces are turned toward him? His body position indicates he is speaking. This is because the only motion you sense is the movement of his hand, which is drawn in a gesture people usually make when they are in the middle of saying something important. Everything else in the picture is motionless and still.

All of these factors emphasize the **centrally positioned figure** and create a sense of seriousness and importance. Can you tell, as you look at the picture, that something momentous is happening?

Draw the main figure in this illustration in the space below. Add in some elements that give your drawing a mood of gravity and significance.

Your drawing:

History Note 11(a) Trace, then write the sentence.

In 1861, the Civil War began when President

Abraham Lincoln went to war with the

Southern states that had seceded from the

Union.

History Note 11(b) Trace, then write the sentence.

In 1861, the Civil War began when President

Abraham Lincoln went to war with the

Southern states that had seceded from the

Union.

Texture

Panning for gold in 1883

This illustration depicts a gold miner searching for gold along a river. Can you tell how the artist created a sense of movement in the composition? He did it by showing us the water flowing into the miner's pan. There is also **texture** suggested by this drawing, a sense of what the surface would feel like if you could touch the water or the rocks on the ground.

Every day, look around carefully. See if you can pick out the textures in all the things around you.

Illustrators pay attention to texture because it lends a sense of realism to their drawings. You could imitate the texture of the rocks and the sand in this illustration by using different kinds of pencil marks.

Spend time experimenting with different pencil marks, creating the texture you like. Try filling a space with small, medium, or large dashes, tiny circles, dots, or long, straight lines. In the space below, see how many different textures you can create right now. Do some areas look rough, like rocks? Or some smooth, like the stones in this river?

Your drawing:

History Note 12(a) Trace, then write the sentence.

In 1865, General Robert E. Lee surrendered

to General Ulysses S. Grant at Appomattox

Court House in Virginia.

History Note 12(b) Trace, then write the sentence.

In 1865, General Robert E. Lee surrendered

to General Ulysses S. Grant at Appomattox

Court House in Virginia.

Symmetry

President Lincoln visits a military camp

The photograph reproduced here is arranged with **symmetry,** that is, if you draw a line down the center from top to bottom, one side of this photograph would almost be a mirror image of the other side.

Notice that President Lincoln is positioned on the line of symmetry and there is a man on either side of him. The tent aligns with the center line, as does the tree directly in the background.

Symmetry is found all over creation. Think of a butterfly whose wings are a perfect mirror image of each other. Think of a branch whose leaves mirror one another. Did you know there is symmetry in your own body? Imagine a line down the center of you. It goes between your eyes, down your nose, and all the way down the length of your body; each side is a mirror image of the other, with matching eyes, arms, and legs. Perhaps we like to see symmetry because we ourselves are symmetrical!

Try to draw this picture of President Lincoln and the two men on either side of him. Or, draw something in nature that is symmetrical.

Your drawing:

History Note 7(c) Review. Trace, then write the sentence.

The War of 1812 gave confidence to the U.S. to

write the Monroe Doctrine, warning Europeans

not to attempt to colonize the Americas.

History Note 8(c) Review. Trace, then write the sentence.

In 1820, Henry Clay worked out the Missouri

Compromise, allowing Missouri to enter the

Union as a slave state and Maine as a free

state.

History Note 9(c) Review. Trace, then write the sentence.

The Compromise of 1850, the Fugitive Slave Act, and the Dred Scott decision preceded the secession of the Southern states.

For practice, draw one of the art lessons again in this space.

History Note 10(c) Review. Trace, then write the sentence.

In 1853, after the Mexican War and the

Gadsden Purchase, President Polk's belief in

the doctrine of Manifest Destiny was realized.

History Note 11(c) Review. Trace, then write the sentence.

In 1861, the Civil War began when President

Abraham Lincoln went to war with the

Southern states that had seceded from the

Union.

History Sentence 12(c) Review. Trace, then write the sentence.

In 1865, General Robert E. Lee surrendered

to General Ulysses S. Grant at Appomattox

Court House in Virginia.

For practice, draw one of the art lessons again in this space.

History Note 13(a) Trace, then write the sentence.

In 1868, the Fourteenth Amendment made

all former slaves U.S. citizens and paved the

way for the Civil Rights Movement.

History Note 13(b) Trace, then write the sentence.

In 1868, the Fourteenth Amendment made

all former slaves U.S. citizens and paved the

way for the Civil Rights Movement.

Presidential Portrait

Ulysses S. Grant

Presidential portrait of Ulysses S. Grant

Since the time of George Washington, the very first president of the United States, presidents have had their portraits painted after their term (or terms) are over. In every **presidential portrait**, the artist attempts to capture the president's character in the way the president poses, in the clothes he wears, and in his expression.

This is the portrait of Ulysses S. Grant. What can you tell about Grant's character from this painting? Well, the stars on his shoulder are part of a military uniform, so you can tell he was probably an important and successful soldier. You might remember him because he is famous for leading the Union army to victory in the Civil War.

How would you describe Grant's expression? See him gazing into the distance? Don't his eyes look a little sad? His mouth is turned down slightly too, almost into a frown. These elements evoke the sense that President Grant was troubled and melancholy.

Perhaps this reflects not just Grant's character but the mood of the United States at the time. People were probably still feeling the terrible consequences of the Civil War and grieving the loss of their loved ones.

Draw President Grant's presidential portrait. Pay particular attention to the elements that convey his personality, character, and mood.

Your drawing:

History Note 14(a) Trace, then write the sentence.

During the late 1800s, tycoons like Vanderbilt,

Rockefeller, Carnegie, and Swift fueled the

nation's Industrial Age by developing

American resources.

History Note 14(b) Trace, then write the sentence.

During the late 1800s, tycoons like Vanderbilt,

Rockefeller, Carnegie, and Swift fueled the

nation's Industrial Age by developing

American resources.

Value

Sewing machine in 1868

If you or someone in your family does a great deal of sewing, you have probably seen a modern sewing machine. They are mostly made of shiny plastic, aren't they? In the 1800s, however, sewing machines were made of metal and wood. This made them much heavier than modern ones.

Look at this drawing of an antique sewing machine. Can you sense how heavy this must be? You get that impression because of the **value** in the drawing. Value refers to how dark or light an artist makes an element in a drawing. See how the artist made this sewing machine very dark? He did it by drawing in many lines to fill the shapes. The areas that remain white (see the vertical lines here and there in the drawing?) make the metal look shiny. Do you see how even the shadow of this sewing machine is dark? It is made up of lots of horizontal lines. This emphasizes the feeling of heaviness in the illustration.

Try sketching this sewing machine, or invent a machine of your own made of metal and wood in the 1800s.

Your drawing:

History Notes 15(a) Trace, then write the sentence.

In 1898, Theodore Roosevelt and his Rough

Riders defeated the Spanish at the Battle of

San Juan Hill while trying to help the

Cubans win their independence.

History Note 15(b) Trace, then write the sentence.

In 1898, Theodore Roosevelt and his Rough

Riders defeated the Spanish at the Battle of

San Juan Hill while trying to help the

Cubans win their independence.

Grouping

Rough Riders charge

Look at this portrayal of Theodore Roosevelt's charging Rough Riders. Isn't it filled with action?

The artist uses **grouping** to organize the elements in this composition. See how the men are arranged in groups of three or five? These are nice numbers to use when you create groups in a drawing. Look to the right. Do you notice the group of five men, all running forward? Then notice there is a group of three men who have been killed. The horse and rider also make up a group because the horse is so big; the horse is like two men! Examine the background. Do you see three more groups of men there? Finally, do you see the lone figure in the center of the composition? Since he is the only man not drawn in a group, he really stands out. He is the one who has just been shot, and the artist captures that moment and emphasizes it by making him the focal point of the composition.

Try drawing this composition or one of your own. Pay attention to the grouping of people in your composition.

Your drawing:

History Note 16(a) Trace, then write the sentence.

From 1820 to 1930, more than 37 million

immigrants came to America, seeking freedom

and the opportunity to increase their

personal wealth.

History Note 16(b) Trace, then write the sentence.

From 1820 to 1930, more than 37 million

immigrants came to America, seeking freedom

and the opportunity to increase their

personal wealth.

Cropping

The torch of the Statue of Liberty in New York

Can you tell that this drawing is a part of the Statue of Liberty? The artist only drew a small part of the statue, but most people know what it is because we are so familiar with this symbol of America.

Drawing just a portion of something is called **cropping**, and it can make an ordinary subject seem much more interesting. This technique can make you feel like you are very close to the subject. You would only get this close to the torch if you were in a helicopter, but the artist makes us feel like we are very near to it by drawing it very large on the page.

You can form a picture frame with your hands to imagine cropping what you see. Do you think you could make an interesting picture using cropping? It can be fun to experiment.

Try drawing this portion of the Statue of Liberty, or try cropping by drawing a portion of something you see around you.

Your drawing:

History Note 17(a) Trace, then write the sentence.

In 1917, President Wilson asked Congress to

declare war on the Central Powers two years

after German U-boats sank the Lusitania,

killing American citizens.

History Note 17(b) Trace, then write the sentence.

In 1917, President Wilson asked Congress to

declare war on the Central Powers two years

after German U-boats sank the Lusitania,

killing American citizens.

Balance

A migrant mother during the Great Depression

In this famous photograph, the artist who snapped the picture has noticed the **balance** naturally occurring in the moment she observed.

Do you see the woman in the center and the children on either side of her? The children create balance in this composition. If there were only one child, the scene would be asymmetrical, and your eye would slide right off of the mother in the picture and onto something else. A balanced composition holds your gaze in a certain place within a composition.

The elements that balance out a composition do not have to be alike, however. Can you see some differences in this picture? How about between the children? Look at their heights and the positions of their hands. These elements in the photograph all show differences.

Try to draw this composition or one you compose yourself using three people to create a balanced composition.

Your drawing:

History Note 18(a) Trace, then write the sentence.

On December 7, 1941, the Japanese bombed Pearl

Harbor, Hawaii, causing the U.S. to join the

Allies in World War II.

History Note 18(b) Trace, then write the sentence.

On December 7, 1941, the Japanese bombed Pearl

Harbor, Hawaii, causing the U.S. to join the

Allies in World War II.

Symbolism

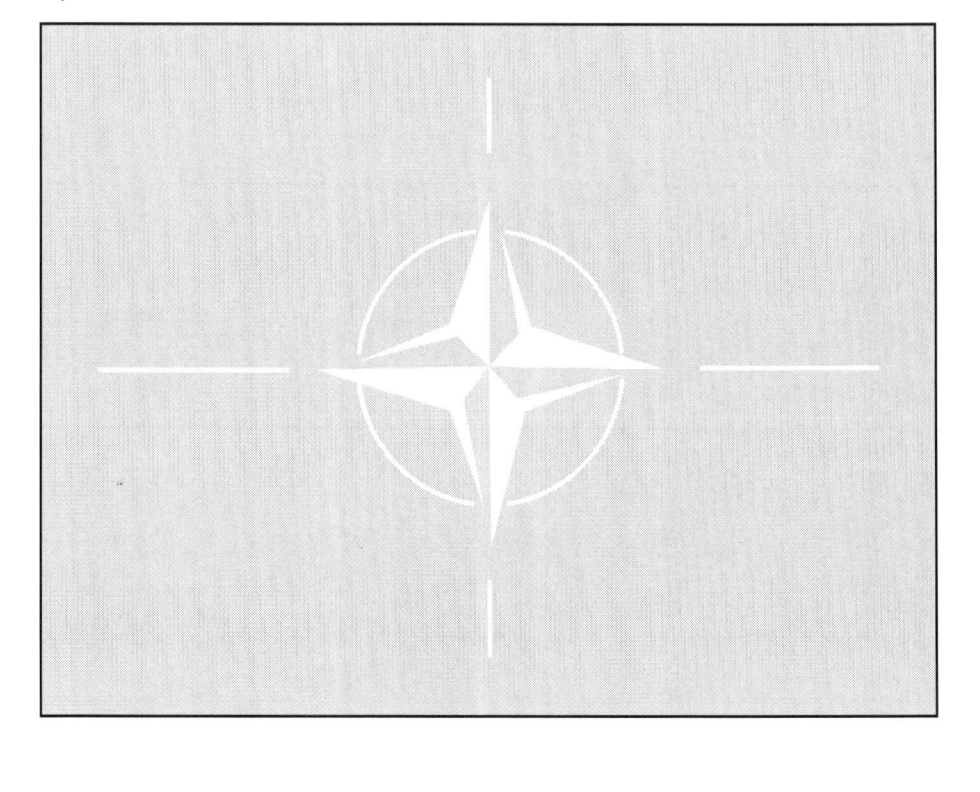

The flag of NATO (North Atlantic Treaty Organization)

This is the flag of NATO, the North Atlantic Treaty Organization. It has a bright blue background with a white star, circle, and lines on it. Flags and artwork often include symbols. **Symbolism** occurs when an artist uses a shape or an item to remind the viewer of something else.

In this composition, the four-pointed star is a symbol for a compass. The compass is a reminder to the members of NATO to keep on the right road—the path of peace. The circle stands for unity; in this case, it represents the unity of the twenty-eight nations who are members of NATO. The blue background is also symbolic. It represents the Atlantic Ocean.

The flag of the United States also contains symbolism. Do you remember that it has thirteen stripes, which represent the original thirteen colonies? It also features fifty stars, which stand for the fifty states that make up the union.

Isn't using symbolism sort of like having a secret code? It can be a fun way to communicate! Many artists, however, make use of the same symbols in the same ways so that the meanings are not secret. The circle representing unity, for example, has been used from antiquity and is often seen in the great cathedrals built in the medieval period.

Try drawing the NATO flag, or using symbolism, design a flag that represents your family.

Your drawing:

History Note 13(c) Review. Trace, then write the sentence.

In 1868, the Fourteenth Amendment made

all former slaves U.S. citizens and paved the

way for the Civil Rights Movement.

History Note 14(c) Review. Trace, then write the sentence.

During the late 1800s, tycoons like Vanderbilt,

Rockefeller, Carnegie, and Swift fueled the

nation's Industrial Age by developing

American resources.

History Sentence 15(c) Review. Trace, then write the sentence.

In 1898, Theodore Roosevelt and his Rough

Riders defeated the Spanish at the Battle of

San Juan Hill while trying to help the

Cubans win their independence.

In this space, draw one of the art lessons again for practice.

History Sentence 16(c) Review. Trace, then write the sentence.

From 1820 to 1930, more than 37 million immigrants came to America, seeking freedom and the opportunity to increase their personal wealth.

History Note 17(c) Review. Trace, then write the sentence.

In 1917, President Wilson asked Congress to

declare war on the Central Powers two years

after German U-boats sank the Lusitania,

killing American citizens.

History Note 18(c) Review. Trace, then write the sentence.

On December 7, 1941, the Japanese bombed Pearl

Harbor, Hawaii, causing the U.S. to join the

Allies in World War II.

For practice, draw one of the art lessons again in this space.

History Note 19(a) Trace, then write the sentence.

In 1949, the U.S. and its allies formed NATO

to resist the spread of Soviet communism.

History Note 19(b) Trace, then write the sentence.

In 1949, the U.S. and its allies formed NATO

to resist the spread of Soviet communism.

Portraiture

Elisabeth and Jim Elliot

This composition features Elisabeth and Jim Elliot, who were missionaries to Ecuador. Jim once wrote, "He is no fool who gives what he cannot keep to gain that which he cannot lose." Jim lost his life trying to teach people about Christ. Elisabeth overcame her grief and ministered to the tribe of people who killed her husband. The tribe members eventually became Christians due to the sacrifices of Jim and Elisabeth. The artist captured them here as they would probably like to be remembered—young, enthusiastic, and full of the love of Christ and His people.

To sketch these **portraits**, or draw the portrait of someone in your family, start by making guidelines. Draw an oval that is slightly flat on the top and narrower at the bottom for the head. Draw a straight line down the middle. This center line will help you place the nose and eyes symmetrically. Draw a straight line through the middle of the oval from left to right. This will be where the eyes should go and where the tops of the ears should be. Draw another straight line between the previous straight line and the chin. This will be where the mouth should go. Fill in the other details by looking closely at the drawing.

Ralph James, a professional artist, offers these additional tips: "Look closely at the person you are drawing as you are establishing the guidelines for the eyes, mouth, etc. Most people vary slightly from those guidelines in some way – for instance, the line for their mouth may be slightly higher or lower. The next most important task to capturing a likeness is to be able to reproduce the light and shadow shapes that make up the subject's face. This will establish the planes of the face, which capture so much of the person's individual 'look'."

Your drawing:

In 1954, in Brown v. Board of Education, the U.S. Supreme Court ruled that the segregation of public schools by race is unconstitutional.

History Note 20(b) Trace, then write the sentence.

In 1954, in Brown v. Board of Education, the

U.S. Supreme Court ruled that the segregation

of public schools by race is unconstitutional.

Perspective

A school for black students in Kansas, 1880

This is a school house in Kansas in 1880. It is drawn using **perspective**, which means it captures the height, width, and depth of the object and gives the impression of distance.

Do you see the side of the building where we can see the entire fireplace? If you line up a ruler with that roof line and draw a line extending about six inches and then you draw a line that aligns with the ground on that side of the building, do you see that the two lines would eventually meet? But if you looked at that side of the building directly, straight on, the lines would be parallel. The same holds true for the front of this building. If you were to extend the line of the top of the front wall, and the line of the bottom of the front wall to the left, these lines would eventually intersect.

Try to sketch this building. First, draw a vertical line as the corner of the building that looks as if it is the closest to you. Then draw long, diagonal guidelines to show how the top of the walls and the bottom of the walls slant. Then, add in the other vertical lines that you see. Add in the details. Following these guidelines should help you create a building that looks very realistic.

Your drawing:

History Note 21(a) Trace, then write the sentence.

In 1969, U.S. astronauts Neil Armstrong and

Edwin Aldrin were the first men to walk on

the moon.

History Note 21(b) Trace, then write the sentence.

In 1969, U.S. astronauts Neil Armstrong and

Edwin Aldrin were the first men to walk on

the moon.

Horizon Line

Edwin "Buzz" Aldrin on the moon

This drawing is a copy of a famous photograph taken by Astronaut Neil Armstrong of Edwin "Buzz" Aldrin on man's first trip to the moon, in 1969. You can't miss the flag in this composition, can you? The flag is in the center, so it is clear that Armstrong thought the flag was the most important element in the composition. He was proud that the United States was the first country to put a man on the moon!

Another important element in this composition is the **horizon line**, the line where the ground meets the sky. It is extremely prominent. See how it is perfectly straight?

Whenever you draw an outdoor scene, you will want to include the horizon line. This might be a straight line where you live, or it might be curvy if you can see hills. It might even be made of angles if you see mountains. There are times when you cannot see a horizon line because trees and buildings stand in the way.

Look outside. Examine how the horizon line is shaped where you are. Draw any scene you see outside with a horizon line, or draw this picture of the flag and astronaut on the moon.

Your drawing:

History Note 22(a) Trace, then write the sentence.

On September 11, 2001, the World Trade Center

in New York City was destroyed by Muslim

terrorists, beginning America's War on

Terrorism.

History Note 22(b) Trace, then write the sentence.

On September 11, 2001, the World Trade Center in New York City was destroyed by Muslim terrorists, beginning America's War on Terrorism.

Perspective

This photograph depicts New York City before the two tall towers of the World Trade Center were destroyed on September 11, 2001. They were called the "twin towers" because they were identical. The towers were so tall, they stood out in any photographs of New York City.

The horizontal line near the bottom of the photograph illustrates where the waterline meets the city harbor. What do the wavy lines below the waterline represent? You're right! They represent the rippling waters of the Hudson River.

Can you see how **perspective** is used to draw this picture? Remember that perspective is a technique that helps artists create the illusion of the height, width, and depth of objects. See how the sides of the buildings in this picture have roof lines that slant down? You know that the roofs are actually flat, but this technique shows that the back sides of the buildings are really farther away.

Try drawing this scene or create your own city in a similar way.

World Trade Center before September 11, 2001

Your drawing:

History Note 23(a) Trace this sentence.

We the People of the United States, in order
to form a more perfect Union, establish justice,
insure domestic Tranquility, provide for the
common defense, promote the general Welfare,
and secure the Blessings of Liberty to ourselves
and our Posterity, do ordain and establish this
Constitution for the United States of America.

History Note 23(b) Trace this sentence.

We the People of the United States, in order to form a more perfect Union, establish Justice, insure domestic Tranquility, provide for the common defense, promote the general Welfare, and secure the Blessings of Liberty to ourselves and our Posterity, do ordain and establish this Constitution for the United States of America.

Engrossing

James Madison

Constitution of the United States

At the time the U.S. Constitution was written, a master penman would have been hired to copy important documents in fine lettering. This was called **engrossing**.

An engrosser wrote with a feather from a goose or a swan. He would cut the tip of the feather to a sharp point with a knife. This made a quill pen. He would dip the point into an inkwell (a small jar filled with ink) and then write with it. When the feather was pulled straight down on the paper, it would make a wide line. When it was pulled to the side, it created a thinner line. In this drawing can you see the wide and thin lines in the first few words of the Constitution?

The engrosser of the U.S. Constitution was Jacob Shallus. He was paid $30 for his engrossing work and wrote all four pages of the document except for the list of states at the end, written by Alexander Hamilton. At one time, there were many engrossers who worked on Capitol Hill, lettering bills that were to be presented in the U.S. Congress.

Draw the first three words of the Constitution as they are shown here. You might like to try drawing with a quill pen sometime, too!

Your drawing:

History Note 24(a) Trace, then write the sentence.

The Bill of Rights are (1) freedoms, (2) own guns,

(3) quartering soldiers, (4) warrants, (5) cannot

testify against self, (6) right to speedy trial, (7)

right to a jury, (8) cruel, unusual punishment,

(9) people's rights, and (10) state's rights.

History Note 24(b) Trace, then write the sentence.

The Bill of Rights are (1) freedoms, (2) own guns,

(3) quartering soldiers, (4) warrants, (5) cannot

testify against self, (6) right to speedy trial, (7)

right to a jury, (8) cruel, unusual punishment,

(9) people's rights, and (10) state's rights.

Symbolism

THE PRESIDENT'S SEAL

E PLURIBUS UNUM

SEAL OF THE PRESIDENT OF THE UNITED STATES

Seal of the President of the United States

You learned about **symbolism** when you drew the flag of NATO earlier. The Seal of the President of the United States uses symbolism, too. Remember that a circle was the symbol for unity? Can you see the fifty stars here, arranged in a circle, representing the fifty states that are unified into one country?

Look at the bald eagle. It is a symbol for the United States. What does the eagle hold in one of its claws? An olive branch, representing peace. What does it hold in the other claw? Arrows, which represent military strength. Look above the eagle. Do you see the thirteen stars and thirteen clouds? What do you think these represent? The original thirteen colonies! These are represented again in the shield in front of the eagle in the thirteen stripes. Notice that the stripes have a bar above them, connecting them all and showing unity and representing Congress. The banner above the eagle includes a Latin phrase: *E pluribus unum*, which means "Out of many, one."

Draw the Presidential Seal below, or design a seal for your family, using symbolism.

Your drawing:

History Note 19(c) Review. Trace, then write the sentence.

In 1949, the U.S. and its allies formed NATO

to resist the spread of Soviet communism.

History Note 20(c) Review. Trace, then write the sentence.

In 1954, in Brown v. Board of Education, the

U.S. Supreme Court ruled that the segregation

of public schools by race is unconstitutional.

History Note 21(c) Review. Trace, then write the sentence.

In 1969, U.S. astronauts Neil Armstrong and
Edwin Aldrin were the first men to walk on
the moon.

For practice, draw one of the art lessons again in this space.

History Note 22(c) Review. Trace, then write the sentence.

On September 11, 2001, the World Trade Center

in New York City was destroyed by Muslim

terrorists, beginning America's War on

Terrorism.

History Note 23(c) Review. Trace this sentence.

We the People of the United States, in order
to form a more perfect Union, establish Justice,
insure domestic Tranquility, provide for the
common defense, promote the general Welfare,
and secure the Blessings of Liberty to ourselves
and our Posterity, do ordain and establish this
Constitution for the United States of America.

History Note 24(c) Review. Trace, then write the sentence.

The Bill of Rights are (1) freedoms, (2) own guns,

(3) quartering soldiers, (4) warrants, (5) cannot

testify against self, (6) right to speedy trial, (7)

right to a jury, (8) cruel, unusual punishment,

(9) people's rights, and (10) state's rights.

For practice, draw one of the art lessons again in this space.

For practice, draw one of the art lessons again in this space.

For practice, draw one of the art lessons again in this space.

For practice, draw one of the art lessons again in this space.

For practice, draw one of the art lessons again in this space.

Image Credits

These coloring illustrations are a rendering of a photograph, piece of artwork, or a public domain image that represents an important historical event or person from American history. Most drawings represent a memory peg image from Classical Conversations® MultiMedia Classical Acts & Facts® History Cards. (The corresponding history card number and title is indicated in parentheses.)

Index of Art Lessons

Additional products from

MULTIMEDIA

Classical Christian Education
Made Approachable

As a modern parent, are you intimidated at the prospect of building a classical, Christian education for your family? Let this booklet show you a blueprint for the tools of learning! Learn how you too can build your family's home-centered, classical education using the building blocks of knowledge, understanding, and wisdom.

Classical Acts & Facts® History Cards

Classical Conversations has developed its own timeline of 161 historical events, representing major cultures on every continent. The events are divided into seven ages and produced as cards similar to our Classical Acts & Facts Science Cards, with the event title on the front and a fuller description of the event on the back. Each card front also contains a beautiful memory peg image. Images were chosen to serve families all the way through cultural studies in the upper levels of Challenge. The back of each card also includes a world map, pinpointing the event location, and a general timeline, illustrating when the event occurred relative to known history.